TRADITIONAL TALES

from

NORTH AMERICA

Vic Parker

Based on myths and legends retold by
Philip Ardagh

Illustrated by
Olivia Rayner

Belitha Press

First published in the UK in 2001 by

Belitha Press Ltd
London House, Great Eastern Wharf,
Parkgate Road, London SW11 4NQ

ISBN 1 84138 175 6

British Library Cataloguing in Publication Data
for this book is available from the British Library.

Editor: Stephanie Turnbull
Designer: Zoë Quayle
Educational consultant: Margaret Bellwood

Printed in Hong Kong

CONTENTS

North American Tales

North America is an enormous continent. It is two and a half times as big as Europe. There are icy, cold lands in the north and towering mountain ranges in the west. In the centre of North America are wide, flat plains of wheat and in the south are hot, dry deserts.

The first people to live in North America came from Asia about 15,000 years ago. Their descendants were the people we call Native Americans. They formed many different groups such as the Cheyenne, Pawnee, Iroquois and Navaho. Each group had its own language and way of life. Some were farmers, others were hunters or warriors. Native Americans shared a great respect for all living things – from people, animals and insects to plants, water and the Earth itself.

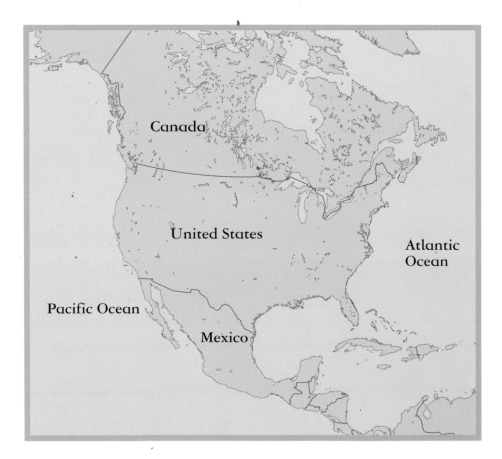

Europeans began to settle in North America about 500 years ago. Spanish and Portuguese explorers came first and they called the Native Americans 'Indians' because they thought they had discovered India. Dutch, Swedish and English people also came to live in North America.

These white people settled all over the country, fighting the Native Americans and driving them off their land. Today, there are not many Native Americans left.

The European settlers brought black people from Africa to work as slaves on North American cotton and tobacco plantations. Slavery was only abolished in 1865. Many of the people living in the United States today are descended from these Africans.

All these groups brought their own myths and legends to North America. You can read new versions of these favourite tales in this book.

5

TALES OF THE GREAT HARE

Long, long ago, when all the world was water, Michabo the Great Hare went swimming. He dived down... down... down... deeper than he had ever swum before. The waters were cold and dark, but the Great Hare kept on swimming.

He swam so far and so deep that he reached the bottom of the ocean and felt the sandy sea bed beneath him. He picked up a single grain of sand and closed his paw tightly around it. The Great Hare then pushed off with his powerful legs and went swimming back upwards, his long ears streaming out behind him.

After a long time, Michabo's head broke through the surface and he floated on the ocean in the sunlight. He opened his paw and watched the tiny grain of sand bob away from him on the waves. Before the Great Hare's eyes, the single grain became a thousand grains... then the thousand grains became a million grains... then the grains formed a patch of land which grew into an island, then a country, then a continent. And still the land kept growing and growing...

Michabo didn't know exactly how big the land became, but one day a wolf cub began to trot across it from one side to the other. The cub loped along for days and weeks and months and years... and by the time he had grown into an adult wolf, he still couldn't see the other side of the land. More years passed and the wolf kept running, but when he was finally old and grey and could run no further, the end of the land was still nowhere in sight. *That's* how big the land was.

The land that the Great Hare had created was in fact what we now call Earth. Many peoples of different tribes and races came to live on it, but the Algonquian-speaking tribes who lived in Northeast America always thought of Michabo as their special friend.

Once, the Great Hare was resting on a river bank when a boy came down to the river to fish. He threw his spear at the silvery, darting creatures time and time again – but they were always too quick for him.

Michabo was so busy watching the boy that he didn't feel a spider creep on to his head. By the time Michabo noticed, the spider had spun a web between his ears!

The web gave the Great Hare an idea for an easier way to catch fish. He took some string and wove a web just like the spider's – except much bigger.

Next he threw his web into the river. When he pulled it out, it was filled with wriggling fish! Because of Michabo's brilliant idea, the people of Northeast America were never short of fish again.

Another time, the Great Hare was lazily playing with a stick when two of his friends walked by. Michabo used his stick to doodle a picture of the man and woman in the earth. He watched the couple go into the forest – and he drew a picture of that, too. Then the Great Hare saw the man and woman coming out of the trees with handfuls of herbs – and he drew a third picture showing just that. When the man and woman walked back past Michabo, they saw the drawings and were delighted.

'Those pictures show us and what we did!' they laughed. 'Anyone who came across them would be able to read them and know what they meant.' And that's how the tribes of Northeast America came to use picture writing.

Michabo the Great Hare taught his human friends many other useful things. They were always sad in winter when the Great Hare went away to his home in the east. There he slept for a long time, but every spring he returned to his people and they were glad.

THE GIANT WOODCUTTER

When Paul Bunyan was born, he had enormous hands and feet and an even bigger appetite!

'That child's going to shoot up into a tall 'un!' said proud Mrs Bunyan. That's exactly what Paul did – faster and taller than she ever imagined.

As a toddler, Paul was as big and strong as a fully-grown man. At eight years old, Paul was so huge that he once sneezed and blew out all the windows in the house. By the time he was old enough to grow a beard everyone had lost track of how tall he was because there was no tape measure long enough to measure him!

When Paul Bunyan finally stopped growing, he was a giant. He was such an agreeable chap, however, that no one was ever afraid of him. In fact, Paul decided to use his great height for the good of the whole town. Everybody needed wood: wood for buildings and furniture, wood for wagons and stables, wood for railway tracks, wood for telegraph poles so people could send messages... the list was endless. Every day the townsmen struggled to cut down the enormous, heavy trees in the forest.

Paul Bunyan decided to lend a hand. He could cut down a tall pine tree with just three swishes of his axe!

The giant set up the finest logging camp for miles around. He chopped down trees so fast it took more than twenty barrels of ink every week to list them all.

When the townspeople had all the wood they could ever want, Paul Bunyan took orders from far and wide across the country. He had to employ hundreds of extra woodcutters to chop wood. There were so many men working at Paul Bunyan's logging camp that Paul had to fill a whole lake with pea soup to feed them. What's more, he had to use such a gigantic pan to fry their pancakes that it could only be greased if two cooks strapped hams to their feet and skated around inside it!

Perhaps the most unusual thing of all was Paul Bunyan's pet – an ox called Babe. Somehow Babe grew to be as enormous as Paul himself and, stranger still, he was bright blue! It was Babe who dragged the trees down the road to the river, so they could be floated downstream to be chopped up at the sawmill. There was just one problem – it was very tricky to get the tall, straight trees down the twisting, zigzagging road.

It wasn't a problem for long.

Paul Bunyan tied Babe's harness to one end of the road and made the ox walk and walk and pull and pull until all the bends and corners were stretched right out. Soon the road was straight from start to finish and the countryside was changed forever!

According to legend, this wasn't the only time Paul Bunyan helped to shape North America. People say the giant once strode along dragging his pickaxe behind him and the rut that it left in the ground was what we now call the Grand Canyon. It's over two hundred miles long and, in places, more than a mile deep! But maybe that's just a very tall story...

CROW AND THE PIECE OF DAYLIGHT

Near the very top of the world lie lands that are covered with snow and ice all year round. Howling winds blow up blinding snowstorms and the air is bitterly cold. These frozen deserts are the lands that the Inuit people call home.

Once, the Inuit lands lay in darkness all year round. The Inuit people hunted polar bears in the darkness. They sat at ice-holes and fished in the darkness. They built igloos in the darkness. There was no dawn or dusk – the sky was always as black as midnight. In fact, the Inuit would never have known what the sun was if it hadn't been for their friend, Crow.

Crow travelled on his wings much, much further than Inuit people could trek on their snowshoes. Crow flew to the very edges of the snow and ice, to where the blackness stopped. Beyond, the skies were bright with daylight. There, Crow soared in the warmth of the sun. He hovered over lands green with forests, purple with mountains, blue with rivers and yellow with patches of sunshine.

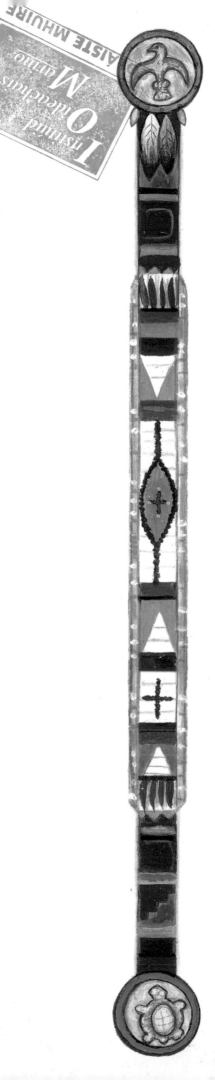

At the end of the day Crow headed back into the dark lands of the Inuit and told the people about the brilliant lands of light.

'Daylight is amazing,' Crow explained. 'It's like lightning, but it isn't gone in a flash. It stays in the sky and lights the world with fabulous colours.'

The Inuit men and women sat in their shadowy igloos and dreamed. They gazed into the blaze of their fires and stared at the light of their seal-oil lamps and imagined how wonderful it would be if their sky were bright all the time.

'Please bring us some of this daylight, Crow,' they begged their friend.

No one saw Crow spring into the air and fly away, for his feathers were as dark as the blackness all around – but by next morning, he was gone.

As Crow flew, he thought about the Inuit people and how good and kind they were. There was so little food in their land that everyone always shared whatever they had. Crow knew that not all people were like that. He was worried that the people who lived in the world of daylight would not want to share any of their precious sunshine with the Inuit – not even a tiny piece.

Suddenly Crow burst out of the blackness and into the light. It wasn't long before he saw a village far below.

He swooped down to the largest, most important-looking house – the house of the chief. Crow landed on a windowsill and peered inside. His beady eyes twinkled when he saw the chief playing with his tiny grandson.

When the chief wasn't looking, Crow flew inside.

'Ask your grandpa for a piece of daylight to play with,' he whispered to the little boy. Then he flew up to the roof and hid there.

'Grandpa! Grandpa!' the excited boy shouted. 'Let me play with a piece of daylight!'

The chief thought that daylight was far too precious to be played with.

'I'll tell you a story instead,' the chief smiled, but tears welled up in the little boy's big eyes. 'I'll let you ride on my back,' the chief promised, but the little boy began to sob. 'I'll let you dress up in my big headdress with a thousand feathers,' the chief said desperately, but the little boy wailed for the daylight.

Finally, the chief gave in. He snapped off a little piece of gleaming daylight. He tied a string to it so it wouldn't blow away and gave the string to his grandson, who beamed with delight. At that very moment Crow swooped down, grabbed the string and flew away as fast as he could, trailing the glowing daylight behind him.

Far away, in the lands of snow and ice, the Inuit saw a distant glimmer of light appear in the black sky. Their hearts leapt for joy as they realized that Crow was returning with a piece of daylight. Slowly, as Crow flapped closer, the whole sky became lighter and brighter. When Crow finally arrived, the snow and ice glittered under bright skies as far as the eye could see.

From that day to this, Crow's small piece of daylight has lit the Inuit lands for half of every year. The rest of the time is as dark as the night. To this day the Inuit people never harm crows – and now you know why.

WILEY AND THE HAIRY MAN

Wiley's mama knew all about things that were magic –
like the Hairy Man in the forest.

'The Hairy Man got your daddy and if you're not careful,
Wiley, he'll get you too!' Wiley's mama often warned.

'I'll be careful,' Wiley promised every time.

Wiley had never once so much as caught a sniff of
the Hairy Man. All the same, he felt better if he had his
two dogs with him when he went into the forest.

One day, Wiley was chopping wood when a pig ran
squealing by and his dogs raced after it. No sooner had
they disappeared among the trees than something huge
and hairy with sharp, pointy teeth came lumbering
towards Wiley. It was the Hairy Man! Wiley saw that
the Hairy Man had cows' hoofs and couldn't climb, so
he shot up a tree as fast as a squirrel.

The Hairy Man stood underneath the branches and
grinned a razor-sharp grin at Wiley.

'Come down and I'll show you some magic,' he said.

'My mama's warned me all about you,' yelled Wiley,
'and I'm not going to fall for that old trick!'

The Hairy Man stopped grinning. He picked up the axe that Wiley had dropped and began to hack away at the tree trunk. Soon the tree would come toppling down.

'Wait a minute, Mr Hairy Man!' cried Wiley, thinking fast. 'Let me say a short prayer before you eat me up.'

'Very well,' frowned the Hairy Man, leaning on the axe.

'Hoooo-eeeeee!' called Wiley at the top of his voice and his two dogs came racing out from the trees, barking and snapping at the Hairy Man.

'Yikes!' gulped the Hairy Man and hurried away.

From that day on, the Hairy Man was determined to catch Wiley. He waited and waited until one day he saw Wiley in the forest without his two dogs. The Hairy Man sprang out of the bushes in front of Wiley. He waggled his hairy eyebrows at the boy and licked his hairy lips.

'Good afternoon, Mr Hairy Man,' said Wiley. 'I'm glad I've bumped into you again, because I've been thinking about what you said and I want to ask you something.'

'Huh?' the Hairy Man shrugged, taken aback.

'You say you can do magic,' continued Wiley. 'So can you make things disappear – like all the rope in the neighbourhood, for instance?'

'Of course,' said the Hairy Man, scrunching up his eyes tightly then opening them again. 'There – it's done!'

'Oh good!' cried Wiley. 'My dogs were tied up but now they'll be free. Hoooo-eeeeee!'

'Yikes!' yelped the Hairy Man and fled into the forest.

Wiley's mama was very proud of her clever son – and she was excited too. She knew that if you could trick a monster three times, he'd have to leave you alone forever.

The next day the Hairy Man came to Wiley's house.

'Where's Wiley?' he bellowed, bashing down the door.

'If I give you my baby, do you promise to leave us alone forever?' demanded Wiley's mama.

'Ummm... yes,' nodded the Hairy Man.

'Then take him,' she said, pointing to Wiley's bed.

The Hairy Man's eyes lit up. He pulled back the sheets and grabbed – not Wiley, but a squirming piglet!

'This isn't your baby!' the Hairy Man growled.

'Oh yes it is!' laughed Wiley's mama. 'I owned the piglet's mother and I own him too – only now he's yours!'

As the Hairy Man howled with fury, Wiley crawled out from his hiding place under the sofa.

'That's the third time we've tricked you, Hairy Man!' he grinned. 'So now you have to leave us alone forever. Hoooo-eeeeee!'

'Yikes!' cried the Hairy Man and Wiley's two dogs chased him all the way back to the forest.

BRER RABBIT AND THE TAR BABY

Brer Fox's greatest wish was to catch Brer Rabbit, but his traps and tricks always failed. That clever rabbit got the better of him every time.

But not this time! chuckled Brer Fox to himself. This time he had a *really* cunning plan. Brer Rabbit wouldn't be walking his bouncy walk and talking his cheeky talk and grinning his saucy grin for much longer!

That night, Brer Fox scooped and patted a big blob of sticky, black tar into the shape of a baby rabbit. Next he put the tar baby slap-bang in the middle of the road, where Brer Rabbit would see it on his morning walk to the lettuce patch. Finally Brer Fox hid in the ditch. All he had to do now was wait...

As the sun rose, Brer Rabbit came bouncing round the corner without a care in the world.

'Good morning!' Brer Rabbit greeted the tar baby. 'It's a fine day, isn't it?'

The tar baby said nothing.

'I said, IT'S A FINE DAY, ISN'T IT?' hollered Brer Rabbit, just in case the tar baby was a little deaf.

The tar baby took no notice.

Brer Rabbit felt rather cross. 'Didn't your folks teach you any manners?' he asked.

The tar baby just ignored him.

This made Brer Rabbit hopping mad. 'You've got until the count of three to say something – or else!' he yelled. 'One... two... three!'

WHACK! Brer Rabbit smacked the tar baby – and his front paw stuck fast like glue. BLAM! He punched with his other paw – and that got stuck too! WHAM! Brer Rabbit kicked the tar baby – and found himself standing on one leg. THWACK! Brer Rabbit kicked again – and there he was, caught good and proper.

Brer Fox leapt out of the ditch and laughed and laughed.

'At last!' he cried with glee. 'I'm going to eat tasty barbecued bunny tonight!'

Brer Rabbit let out a huge sigh of relief. 'Oh, thank goodness!' he gasped.

Brer Fox's face fell. 'Aren't you worried?' he growled.

'I can think of worse things than being roasted,' smirked Brer Rabbit.

'All right, I'll drown you instead!' yelled Brer Fox.

'What a relief!' Brer Rabbit chuckled. 'Drowning is still not all that bad.'

'I'll string you up by the tail, then!' screamed Brer Fox.

'Do anything you like, Brer Fox,' beamed Brer Rabbit, 'just don't hurl me into the nasty, thorny briar patch. That would be the very worst thing you could do to me!'

'Right!' Brer Fox roared. 'The briar patch it is, then!'

He grabbed Brer Rabbit by the ears, pulled him off the tar baby and flung him into the air. Brer Rabbit came down – BUMP! – right in the thorny briar patch.

'Hee hee!' Brer Rabbit giggled, jumping up and dusting himself off. 'I was born and bred in a briar patch, Brer Fox!'

Brer Fox had been tricked again! And while he howled with anger, Brer Rabbit bounced happily all the way to the lettuce patch.

THE SEARCH FOR HEALING

One winter, it wasn't just the snow and ice that came to stay at the village of the Iroquois people – a terrible sickness came too. The medicine man could do nothing to send it away. The sickness visited every wigwam and struck down several members in each family. Day after day, the sound of wailing filled the air as more men, women and children breathed their last breath. Those still living grew exhausted and full of despair.

A warrior called Nekumonta watched each of his relations grow pale and then die from the terrible sickness. Before long, only his beautiful wife Shanewis was left – and she became ill too. Nekumonta did his best to care for Shanewis, but there was nothing he could do to make her better. The warrior felt helpless and angry.

Finally, the dreaded day arrived when Shanewis heard the voices of her dead ancestors calling her to take her place among them.

'My darling wife, you must not die and leave me,' sobbed Nekumonta. 'I will try to find the healing herbs of the Manitou – they will surely save you.'

The Manitou was the greatest and most powerful of the Iroquois gods. There was an ancient story that the Manitou had planted herbs which would cure all ills – but no one knew where they grew.

'Beautiful Shanewis,' Nekumonta whispered. 'Hold on until I return from my journey!'

'I will try,' Shanewis murmured weakly.

Nekumonta hurried off at once into the forest. He had no idea what the Manitou's healing plants might look like or where they might grow. Time after time, the desperate man plunged his hands into the freezing snow and dug deep, hoping to find the magic herbs.

The squirrels and deer and other creatures of the forest came out of their hiding places to see what Nekumonta was doing. They knew Nekumonta and weren't afraid of him. Though other men liked to hunt woodland animals for sport, Nekumonta had always treated all creatures with kindness and respect.

'Do you know where the Manitou has planted the herbs that will heal my people?' Nekumonta begged the creatures. None of them did. They crept back into the woods, sad that they were unable to help their friend.

Nekumonta searched for three days without success. By the end of the third day, he was freezing and starving.

He felt that he was no nearer finding the Manitou's herbs than before and his tired head was full of thoughts of his beloved, dying Shanewis. As the cold sun sank down into the earth, he huddled under his blankets and sank into nightmares.

While Nekumonta tossed and turned, the animals of the forest held a meeting.

'This Iroquois warrior is a good human,' said the bear.

'Yes,' agreed the rabbit. 'He has never once been cruel to us or damaged our homes.'

'He deserves our help,' the deer insisted. 'Whatever can we do?'

'We can't do anything,' pointed out the beaver, 'but the great Manitou himself can. Perhaps if we all ask him, he will realize how much every living thing wants Nekumonta to succeed in his brave quest.'

Under the light of the full moon, the woodland creatures gathered in a clearing in the forest and cried out to the Manitou. The great god was extremely surprised to hear so many animals praying as one – particularly as they were asking for help for a human! The Manitou was moved by their loyalty and decided to grant their wish. He would help Nekumonta.

The Manitou sent the man a dream of his dying wife.

Softly, she sang a beautiful song that turned into a chorus of voices. The singing sounded like the music of a waterfall – and when Nekumonta awoke, he could still hear it.

'We are the healing waters...' the voices sang. 'Find us... Free us... then Shanewis and your people will be saved.'

Suddenly, Nekumonta felt a surge of hope. He hunted high and low and at last realized where the singing was coming from – an underground spring beneath his feet!

The forest creatures watched anxiously as Nekumonta scraped and scrabbled in the dirt, then – WHOOSH! A fountain of crystal water gushed into the air and bubbled away in a stream down the hillside. It splashed over Nekumonta and he at once felt energy flooding into his body. The waters were magic!

Nekumonta's heart thumped inside his chest as he filled a skin bottle with the healing waters and raced back to his village. Soon, his lovely wife's eyes were bright and sparkling once again and it wasn't long before every other sick person was healed too.

Nekumonta's kindness to the animals had been repaid and everyone gave thanks with all their hearts to the great and good Manitou.

TALES OF DAVY CROCKETT

Davy Crockett wore a racoon-fur hat and a deerskin jacket and lived all by himself in a log cabin in the forest. Most white settlers would have been terrified to live on their own in the wilderness, where they might meet Native American warriors or wild animals, but Davy Crockett seemed to be perfectly at home there.

People said that Davy Crockett could listen to a twig snap and tell you which animal was approaching. Stories spread that Davy Crockett could scare racoons out of the trees just by grinning at them. News went round that Davy Crockett had killed a hundred and one bears in just one year and that now bears turned tail and fled whenever they sniffed Davy Crockett's scent on the wind. But there was once a time when an animal got the better of Davy Crockett...

Davy Crockett was hunting in the woods one day when a racoon scampered into the clearing right in front of him. The startled animal looked at the man and his gun and gulped.

'Eeek! It's Davy Crockett!' the racoon yelped.

'Yep, that's right,' replied Davy Crockett proudly, raising his gun and taking aim.

The racoon took a deep breath.

'It would be an honour to be shot by you, Mr Crockett,' he announced. 'You're the finest hunter these woods have ever known. Please fire away.'

Davy Crockett was deeply moved by the little animal's compliment. A tear glistened in his eye and he lowered his gun.

'Why, thank you very much,' he told the racoon. 'After what you've just said, I don't think I'll shoot you after all.'

'I'll be off then,' called the racoon cheerily, 'just in case you change your mind. Nice to meet you, Mr Crockett!'

He scampered into the bushes and was gone.

Davy Crockett scratched his head and thought for a moment. He began to grin... then he threw back his head and laughed.

'I do believe that animal has just tricked me!' he guffawed. 'That was the cleverest racoon I've ever met!'

It was the one and only time that Davy Crockett was ever outsmarted. He was such an excellent hunter and tracker that he became famous far and wide. People started to call him the King of the Wild Frontier.

Davy Crockett became a hero to the people of North America. There's even a story of how he once saved everyone from being burnt to a crisp when a shooting star called Halley's Comet came speeding towards the Earth. People said that Davy Crockett grabbed the comet by its fiery tail and hurled it back into space, where it could cause no harm.

Davy Crockett died about two hundred years ago, but today in North America people still enjoy telling tales of his amazing deeds – just like the ones here.

THE BABY
AND THE GOD

The god Glooskap was a great warrior. He fought
many wars and won every battle – not just with
strength and bravery, but with wit and cunning too.

Glooskap spent many years away fighting. By the
time he finally returned home, all his success and fame
had made him rather bigheaded.

'There's no one left in the world who doesn't fear
me and won't obey me,' he boasted.

'Oh yes there is,' piped up a woman, boldly 'I know
someone who doesn't fear you – and he certainly won't
obey you!'

'Who cannot have heard of the great Glooskap?' the
annoyed god roared. 'Who is it that dares not tremble
before my name?'

'His name is Wasis,' the woman calmly replied.

Hmmm, Wasis... thought Glooskap. No, he was certain
he had never heard of any warrior chief called Wasis on
all his travels.

'Are you sure about this?' asked the puzzled Glooskap.

'Quite sure,' said the woman, with a twinkle in her eye.

'Wasis always does exactly what he pleases. He won't obey anyone – not even you, master.'

'Then this Wasis must be very mighty,' said Glooskap. 'Is he as tall as the Kewawkqu'?' The Kewawkqu' were a race of giants. 'Is his magic greater than the Medecolin?' The Medecolin were cunning magicians. 'Is he as wicked as Pamola?' Pamola was an evil spirit of the night.

'Wasis is smaller than a goblin,' said the woman. 'He knows no magic and there is no wickedness in him at all.'

Glooskap was baffled. 'So there's nothing special about this Wasis and yet he would challenge me!' he exclaimed. 'I must see him for myself and teach him a lesson. Take me to him!'

'Wasis lives close by,' said the woman. 'Follow me.'

The woman led the god among the wigwams belonging to her neighbours.

'Does Wasis live here in the village, among the ordinary folk?' asked the puzzled Glooskap.

The woman said nothing, but took Glooskap to her very own home.

'But this is where you live,' exclaimed Glooskap, surprised.

'Yes, and now Wasis lives here too,' said the woman and she led the god inside.

Glooskap peered around. 'Where is he?' he shrugged.

'There,' said the woman and she pointed to a baby who sat on a rug, sucking a piece of maple sugar.

'That is Wasis?' cried Glooskap. He threw back his head and roared with laughter.

'Yes. Wasis is my son,' smiled the woman. She knew that the great warrior god understood all about exploring and adventuring and fighting, but he had no idea about babies. He had never even met one before!

'Come here, Wasis,' Glooskap cooed. He bent forward and held out his arms.

The baby's eyes opened wide and he smiled at the strange man. Then he went straight back to sucking the piece of maple sugar he held in his fat little fist.

'Hmph,' said Glooskap, rather annoyed. It was the first time anyone had ever failed to do as he said straight away, but he didn't give up. The clever god cupped his hands to his mouth and whistled a beautiful bird song.

'Wonderful!' breathed the woman, but Wasis took no notice of Glooskap's music at all. It was as if he had suddenly gone deaf.

Glooskap was furious. 'Come here!' he roared, stamping his foot and waving his arms. 'Come here at once!'

Wasis looked up and stared straight at Glooskap.

For a moment, the god thought the baby was finally going to crawl towards him. Instead Wasis opened his mouth wide and began to scream.

'Be quiet!' raged Glooskap, as purple-faced as the baby. 'Be silent and come here! I command you!'

The louder Glooskap shouted, the louder Wasis howled and wailed... and still he sat on the same spot on the rug.

Finally, Glooskap used his magic. He sang a song of enchantment so powerful that some people said evil spirits scurried to the depths of the Earth to escape it. At last Wasis stopped howling and listened. He blinked his tearful eyes and began to grin. Soothed by Glooskap's music, the baby's little eyelids began to droop. Instead of crawling to the god, Wasis started to fall asleep.

With a roar of rage that could be heard for miles around, Glooskap gave up and stormed out of the wigwam. The woman smiled to herself and scooped Wasis up off the floor.

'I think you've taught the mighty Glooskap a lesson today,' she whispered as she cuddled her baby close.

'Goo!' replied Wasis, trying to say Glooskap's name – and babies still say 'Goo!' today, to remind us of the time when the greatest of gods was put firmly in his place by the smallest of children.

WHEN PEOPLE HAD WINGS

'I wonder how hot the sun is back home in Africa,' whispered John. Sweat trickled off his forehead and soaked his shirt as he picked cotton off the plants.

Mary sighed. 'There we'd be working for ourselves,' she replied, under her breath. 'We'd be feeding our families instead of making money for these white men.'

Every day, it was the same. The African slaves were beaten awake at sunrise and marched to the cotton fields without any breakfast. By sundown, their whole bodies were aching and their stomachs burned with hunger. They hobbled back for a bowl of thin soup and a crust of stale bread, while inside the big house the Master was served a delicious dinner from silver dishes.

'I wish I had my papa's wings so I could fly away,' murmured Tom.

'Whatever do you mean?' whispered John in surprise.

'I mean what I said – I wish I had my papa's wings,' hissed Tom.

The slaves fell silent as they heard the pounding of the Overseer's horse coming up close behind them.

The Overseer rode up and down the fields all day checking that the men and women were working hard. Anyone found talking was silenced by a lash of his whip.

The Overseer moved away and Tom whispered, 'Didn't you know that when our papas and mamas lived in Africa, they had wings and could fly?'

Mary and John shook their heads in amazement.

'Oh yes,' sighed Tom. 'They had beautiful, black wings and they soared through the skies, free as birds.'

'What happened to them?' whispered Mary.

'When the white people forced our mamas and papas on to boats and brought them across the ocean, they were so miserable that they lost the power to fly,' explained Tom sadly. 'Their wings just shrivelled up and died and when we were born, we didn't have wings at all.'

All day long, Mary and John thought about flying. They wondered what it would be like to hover in the heat of the African sun. They tried to imagine how it would feel to swoop through the bright skies of their homeland.

That night, when John was asleep in his hard bunk, he dreamed that he cried out loud for wings. A wrinkled, old man appeared by his bedside and shook him awake.

'I am the One Who Remembers,' the man said, his eyes shining. 'Wake the others and come outside.'

Soon all the slaves were gathered in the chill moonlight.

'Join hands,' instructed the old man, so the men and women huddled closer and linked their fingers. The old man shut his eyes and chanted some mysterious words.

A shiver ran down the spine of each and every slave as their back muscles seemed to ripple with strange energy. Suddenly they felt huge wings rip through the cloth of their shirts. With a few powerful wingbeats, all the slaves soared into the dark air. They were free!

Next morning, the Overseer found that his slaves had vanished without a trace. Only a handful of long, black feathers were tumbling in the wind over the dust...

THE STORY OF DEATH

The Maidu people believe that at the beginning of time, the gods Kodoyanpe and Coyote floated on the surface of a huge ocean and created all things. They created the land, plants and animals. They created people – so many that the two gods became worried.

'What shall we do?' Kodoyanpe said to Coyote. 'Our people are having lots of children. They bring joy and happiness and hope for the future, but there isn't enough space on the Earth for so many people.'

'Plants die,' Coyote said thoughtfully. 'Animals die. Why shouldn't humans die too?'

Kodoyanpe looked worried. 'That would be cruel,' he said in a low voice. 'It would make humans very unhappy if their loved ones went away from the Earth forever.'

'Well, have you got a better idea?' snapped Coyote.

The Caddo people believe that Kodoyanpe decided that people should die after all, but that their spirits should leave the Earth and stay in a special house. After a while the spirits would be able to come back to life in a new body.

However, the Caddo people say that when the first person died, Coyote turned himself into a wild dog. He blocked the entrance to the house and wouldn't let the spirit inside. The soul wandered the skies until he came to the land of the spirits, from which there is no return. This is the way it has been with humans ever since.

The Maidu people tell a different story. They say that the quarrelsome Coyote just argued and argued with Kodoyanpe until he got his way. People would die and leave Earth forever.

We will ever know which story is true, but it doesn't really matter. The result was the same – death came to mean the end of life on Earth for humans.

After Kodoyanpe and Coyote had argued over death, they went their separate ways to live among humans. Kodoyanpe loved living among the people he had created. Coyote, on the other hand, didn't care about anyone – until his son was born. As Coyote looked at his little boy, he felt love for the first time. As the child grew older, he brought Coyote joy and happiness and hope for the future, just as Kodoyanpe had said children did.

But one day Coyote's son was bitten by a snake.

'Father, I am dying,' the little boy gasped as the poison chilled his veins. 'Help me!'

Coyote threw back his head and howled in anguish. He snatched up his son and raced like the wind over the Earth until he found Kodoyanpe.

'I was wrong about death!' Coyote wailed. 'Death shouldn't be the end of things. I can't bear to live without my son. Is there anything we can do?'

Kodoyanpe wept as he watched life leave the little child's body.

'It was you who wanted death to be the end,' he whispered. 'What's done is done. We cannot undo it.'

Coyote howled another bloodcurdling cry of pain. As he did so, he crouched down on all fours. His body became hunched and hairy. He scowled an ugly sneer and his tongue lolled out of sharp-toothed jaws. Claws sprang from his feet and his eyes flashed with yellow fire.

'I think you knew a way to save my son,' Coyote snarled. 'I think you just didn't want to! I shan't forget this, brother!'

Coyote sprang across the world in his new form, filled with bitterness and hatred. He roamed the Earth, stirring up trouble and making as much mischief as possible.

Kodoyanpe shook his head in despair when he saw the misery Coyote was causing his people.

'Build a giant canoe,' Kodoyanpe secretly told the people. 'Make it big enough for everyone to fit inside.'

All over the Earth, people worked together to build the enormous canoe. They clambered aboard and then Kodoyanpe created the biggest storm the world had ever seen. The sky was blotted out with black storm clouds. Lightning zigzagged through the darkness and thunder crashed through the heavens. Waterfalls came pouring out of the skies, swelling the rivers and lakes and seas until they joined together as one huge ocean. Kodoyanpe was going to drown Coyote by flooding the world.

When the rains finally stopped, Kodoyanpe looked all around and saw that everywhere was water. The only land that remained poking up above the waves was the very tips of the highest mountains – and there on one of them was the laughing Coyote! The cunning god had disguised himself as a person and crept into the canoe with everybody else. As the giant boat had swept past a rocky peak, crafty Coyote had jumped out on to it.

Kodoyanpe's plan had failed. To this day Coyote is still out there somewhere – which is why we have evil in the world.

INDEX